Unlocking H

CW00531400

A Comprehensive Guide to Trauma Treatment

Theodora Brooks

Trauma Treatment Toolbox

This document is geared towards providing exact and reliable information with regards to the topic and issue covered. The publication is sold with the idea that the publisher is not required to render accounting, officially permitted, or otherwise, qualified services. If advice is necessary, legal or professional, a practiced individual in the profession should be ordered.

From a Declaration of Principles which was accepted and approved equally by a Committee of the American Bar Association and a Committee of Publishers and Associations.

are for clarifying purposes only and are owned by the owners themselves, not affiliated with this document.

TABLE OF CONTENTS

CHAPTER 1: TRAUMA TREATMENT TOOLBOX

Trauma is a complex and multifaceted experience that affects individuals in profound ways. It's not something that can be neatly categorized or easily understood. To effectively address trauma and support those who have experienced it, we must equip ourselves with a toolbox filled with knowledge, empathy, and a range of therapeutic approaches.

1.1 The Impact of Trauma on the Brain and Body

Trauma leaves a lasting imprint on the brain and body, reshaping the way individuals perceive and respond to the world around them. Understanding this impact is crucial for trauma treatment.

When a person experiences trauma, the brain's stress response system goes into overdrive. The amygdala, our brain's alarm system, becomes hyperactive, leading to heightened states of alertness and anxiety. The hippocampus, responsible for memory and context, struggles to process traumatic memories properly. As a result, trauma survivors may experience flashbacks, nightmares, and a constant state of hypervigilance.

Furthermore, chronic trauma can lead to changes in the brain's structure and function. The prefrontal cortex, responsible for decision-making and emotional regulation, can become compromised. This can result in impulsive behavior, mood swings, and difficulty in managing emotions.

Understanding these neurological changes is the first step in developing effective trauma treatment strategies. Therapists armed with this knowledge can tailor interventions to help clients regain a sense of control over their brain and body responses. Techniques like mindfulness, cognitive-behavioral therapy, and neurofeedback can be powerful tools in reestablishing equilibrium.

1.2 Types and Causes of Trauma

Trauma comes in many forms and can be caused by a wide range of events and experiences. Recognizing the diversity of trauma is essential for providing effective treatment.

There are several common types of trauma, including:

1. Acute Trauma: This results from a single, often life-threatening event, such as a car accident or natural disaster.

2. Chronic Trauma: Ongoing, repetitive stressors like domestic violence, bullying, or long-term medical conditions can lead to chronic trauma.

3. Complex Trauma: This type results from exposure to multiple traumatic events, often in childhood, such as neglect, abuse, or witnessing domestic violence.

4. Developmental Trauma: Trauma that occurs during critical stages of development can lead to long-lasting psychological and emotional challenges.

5. Secondary Trauma: Professionals who work with trauma survivors, like therapists or first responders,

can experience secondary trauma, also known as vicarious trauma.

Understanding the different types of trauma helps therapists tailor their approach to the unique needs of each client. It's also essential to recognize that trauma can be caused by a wide range of events, not just the stereotypical "big" traumas. Everyday experiences, such as workplace harassment, discrimination, or the loss of a loved one, can also lead to trauma.

1.3 Recognizing the Signs and Symptoms of Trauma

Identifying trauma in individuals who may not readily disclose their experiences is a critical skill for therapists. Trauma often remains hidden beneath the surface, masked by coping mechanisms and avoidance strategies.

Common signs and symptoms of trauma include:

- Hyperarousal: Individuals may display heightened reactivity, including anger, irritability, and a heightened startle response.

- Hypervigilance: Constantly scanning the environment for threats and danger.

- Avoidance: Efforts to avoid situations, people, or places that trigger traumatic memories.

- Reexperiencing: Flashbacks, nightmares, and intrusive thoughts related to the trauma.

- Emotional numbness: A sense of detachment and an inability to connect with others emotionally.

- Physical symptoms: Trauma can manifest as physical ailments, such as headaches, stomachaches, or unexplained pain.

Recognizing these signs and symptoms is vital for early intervention and support. By creating a safe and empathetic space, therapists can encourage trauma survivors to share their experiences and begin the journey toward healing.

In this chapter, we've laid the foundation for understanding trauma. Armed with knowledge about its impact on the brain and body, the various types and causes of trauma, and the signs and symptoms to look for, we are better prepared to explore the tools and techniques needed for effective trauma treatment. In the chapters ahead, we'll delve deeper into the trauma treatment toolbox, offering a range

of strategies to help individuals on their path to

healing and recovery.

Chapter 2: Assessment and Diagnosis

In the journey to healing from trauma, a thorough and sensitive assessment is the compass that guides treatment. The process of assessment and diagnosis not only helps therapists understand the nature and extent of trauma but also informs the choice of appropriate therapeutic interventions. In this chapter, we will explore the key components of the Trauma Treatment Toolbox that relate to assessment and diagnosis.

2.1 Trauma-Informed Assessment Tools

Assessing trauma requires more than a checklist of symptoms. It demands a trauma-informed approach that prioritizes safety, empowerment, and collaboration. Several assessment tools and techniques facilitate this process:

Clinical Interviews: The cornerstone of trauma assessment is the clinical interview. These conversations are structured to create a safe environment where clients can share their experiences and feelings. Open-ended questions, active listening, and empathetic responses help clients feel heard and validated.

Trauma Questionnaires: Several standardized questionnaires, such as the PTSD Checklist for DSM-5 (PCL-5) and the Adverse Childhood Experiences (ACE) questionnaire, are widely used in trauma assessment. These tools provide quantitative data and help therapists gauge the severity of trauma symptoms.

Cultural Assessment: Cultural competence is vital in trauma assessment. Clients from diverse backgrounds may have unique expressions of trauma and varying levels of comfort in discussing it. Understanding cultural norms and beliefs helps therapists tailor their approach and questions to be sensitive and respectful.

Resilience and Strengths Assessment: In addition to assessing trauma symptoms, it's crucial to identify a client's strengths and resilience factors. This helps in crafting a treatment plan that leverages these assets in the healing process.

Trauma-informed assessment tools go beyond labeling and diagnosing trauma; they serve as a foundation for building trust and rapport between therapist and client.

2.2 Differential Diagnosis in Trauma Treatment

Trauma symptoms often overlap with other mental health conditions, making differential diagnosis a critical aspect of assessment. It's not uncommon for clients to present with symptoms that could be attributed to conditions like depression, anxiety, or substance use disorders. Here are some key considerations in this process:

Complexity of Presentation: Trauma's impact on the mind and body can manifest in myriad ways. Clients may exhibit symptoms that are not directly related to trauma but are a result of its pervasive effects. A comprehensive assessment takes into account the complexity of these presentations.

Comorbidity: Trauma is often accompanied by other mental health conditions. Clients with a history of trauma may be at a higher risk of developing conditions such as depression, anxiety, or substance use disorders. Differential diagnosis helps identify and address these comorbidities.

Trauma-Related Disorders: Beyond post-traumatic stress disorder (PTSD), trauma can lead to other disorders like complex PTSD or dissociative disorders. Thorough assessment allows for the identification of these specific trauma-related conditions.

Trauma Mimics: Some medical conditions or medication side effects can mimic trauma symptoms. It's essential for therapists to consider these factors during the assessment process to ensure an accurate diagnosis.

Collaborative Assessment: Collaborating with other healthcare professionals, such as physicians and psychiatrists, can be invaluable in differentia diagnosis. A multidisciplinary approach ensures that all aspects of a client's health are considered.

Differential diagnosis serves as the compass that guides treatment planning. It ensures that clients receive the right interventions tailored to their specific needs, whether those needs are primarily related to trauma or involve comorbid conditions.

2.3 Cultural Sensitivity in Trauma Assessment

Cultural sensitivity is a fundamental aspect of trauma assessment. Trauma is a universal human experience, but its expression can be deeply influenced by cultural factors, beliefs, and norms. To conduct trauma assessments effectively, therapists must consider cultural sensitivity:

Cultural Awareness: Therapists must be aware of their own cultural biases and assumptions. Self-awareness helps prevent inadvertently imposing one's beliefs on clients and allows for a more open and respectful dialogue.

Cultural Competence: Being culturally competent means actively seeking knowledge about different cultural backgrounds and their impact on trauma experiences. Therapists can educate themselves about cultural norms, beliefs, and expressions of distress.

Language and Communication: Language barriers can hinder effective assessment. Providing interpreters or using culturally appropriate communication tools can bridge these gaps.

Cultural Trauma: Some communities may have experienced historical or collective trauma related to their culture or ethnicity. Understanding these dynamics is essential for trauma assessment.

Trust and Rapport: Cultural sensitivity fosters trust and rapport between therapist and client. Clients are more likely to open up and engage in the assessment process when they feel understood and respected within their cultural context.

CHAPTER 3: BUILDING A THERAPEUTIC RELATIONSHIP

In the realm of trauma treatment, the therapeutic relationship is the cornerstone upon which healing is constructed. Establishing a strong and secure connection between therapist and client is pivotal to the recovery process. This chapter delves into the essential elements of building a therapeutic relationship within the Trauma Treatment Toolbox.

3.1 Establishing Trust and Safety

Trauma survivors often grapple with a profound sense of mistrust. Their traumatic experiences may have shattered their belief in safety and security.

Therefore, the therapist's first task is to create an environment where trust can be rebuilt and safety can be restored.

- Empathy and Active Listening: Listening without judgment and demonstrating empathy are powerful tools in establishing trust. Clients need to feel heard and understood.

- Transparency: Being transparent about the therapy process, goals, and what clients can expect helps demystify the therapeutic journey, reducing anxiety and uncertainty.

- Consistency: Maintaining consistent appointment schedules and boundaries instills a sense of reliability which is crucial for rebuilding trust.

- Collaboration: Involving clients in treatment decisions and goal-setting empowers them and reinforces their sense of agency and control.

- Crisis Management: Preparing for potential crises and having a plan in place for handling them can reassure clients that their safety is a top priority.

Creating a safe and trusting therapeutic space lays the foundation for all subsequent therapeutic work.

3.2 Communication Strategies in Trauma Therapy

Effective communication is the lifeblood of the therapeutic relationship. In trauma therapy, it takes on added significance because trauma survivors often struggle with verbalizing their experiences and emotions. Therapists must employ specific strategies to facilitate open and honest communication:

- Psychoeducation: Providing clients with information about trauma and its effects can help them understand their experiences better.

- Nonverbal Cues: Paying attention to nonverbal cues, such as body language and facial expressions, can reveal unspoken feelings and thoughts.

- Active Engagement: Encouraging clients to express themselves actively rather than passively receiving therapy helps them take ownership of their healing process.

- Validation: Validating clients' emotions and experiences, even if they seem irrational or confusing, helps them feel understood and accepted.

- Trauma-Informed Language: Using trauma-informed language that avoids blame or judgment is essential. Instead of asking, "Why did you do that?" therapists might ask, "What led to that decision?"

- Trauma Narration: Gradually guiding clients through the process of recounting their traumatic experiences can be a powerful tool for processing and healing.

- Respect for Silence: Silence can be a vital part of trauma therapy, allowing clients the space to reflect and process their thoughts and emotions.

Effective communication is a dance between therapist and client, one that requires sensitivity, patience, and a deep understanding of the client's unique needs.

3.3 Boundaries and Ethics in Trauma Treatment

Maintaining clear and ethical boundaries is non-negotiable in trauma therapy. Clients who have experienced trauma may have blurred boundaries due to their experiences, making it even more crucial for therapists to establish and uphold clear therapeutic boundaries. Here are key considerations:

- Informed Consent: Clearly explaining the therapy process, including its limits and expectations, ensures that clients give informed consent.

- Dual Relationships: Avoiding dual relationships, where the therapist plays multiple roles in the client's life, is essential to prevent conflicts of interest.

- Confidentiality: Ensuring the confidentiality of client information builds trust. Therapists must explain the exceptions to confidentiality, such as mandated reporting of abuse or imminent harm to self or others.

- Self-Care: Therapists must prioritize their own self-care to prevent burnout and maintain their ability to provide effective therapy.

- Cultural Competence: Understanding and respecting cultural differences is essential to maintaining ethical boundaries.

- Supervision: Regular supervision and consultation with peers and supervisors help therapists maintain ethical standards and address any ethical dilemmas that may arise.

Boundaries are not restrictions but safeguards that protect both the client and the therapist. They create a container within which the therapeutic work can flourish.

In conclusion, building a therapeutic relationship in trauma treatment is an art and a science. It requires the delicate balance of creating trust and safety, employing effective communication strategies, and upholding ethical boundaries. This relationship is the vessel in which healing takes place, and it must be nurtured and prioritized throughout the therapeutic journey.

Chapter 4: Evidence-Based Approaches

When it comes to treating trauma, it's crucial to have a toolbox filled with evidence-based approaches that have proven effectiveness. This chapter explores three such approaches that have been widely used and studied in trauma therapy: Cognitive-Behavioral Therapy (CBT) for Trauma, Eye Movement Desensitization and Reprocessing (EMDR), and Trauma-Focused Play Therapy for Children.

4.1 Cognitive-Behavioral Therapy for Trauma

Cognitive-Behavioral Therapy (CBT) has long been recognized as one of the most effective approaches to trauma treatment. It's based on the idea that our thoughts, feelings, and behaviors are interconnected, and by changing negative thought patterns, we can alleviate emotional distress and maladaptive behaviors. In the context of trauma treatment, CBT focuses on several key elements:

- Education: Clients learn about the connection between their thoughts, feelings, and behaviors, helping them understand the impact of trauma on their cognitive processes.

- Exposure Therapy: Gradual exposure to trauma-related memories and situations helps desensitize clients to their triggers.

- Cognitive Restructuring: Identifying and challenging negative thought patterns, such as self-blame or catastrophic thinking, is a central component of CBT.

- Skill-Building: Clients learn coping skills to manage distressing emotions and develop healthier ways of responding to triggers.

CBT for trauma is a structured, time-limited approach that can be highly effective in helping clients gain control over their trauma-related symptoms and lead more fulfilling lives.

4.2 Eye Movement Desensitization and Reprocessing (EMDR)

Eye Movement Desensitization and Reprocessing (EMDR) is a specialized therapy designed to help clients process traumatic memories and reduce their emotional charge. EMDR is based on the idea that traumatic memories are not fully processed and can become "stuck" in the brain, leading to distressing symptoms. EMDR includes the following key components:

- Bilateral Stimulation: During EMDR sessions, clients focus on distressing memories while simultaneously engaging in bilateral stimulation, typically through rapid eye movements. This process is believed to help reprocess traumatic memories.

- Phases of Treatment: EMDR is typically structured into several phases, including history-taking, preparation, assessment, desensitization, installation of positive beliefs, and closure. Each phase serves a specific purpose in the therapeutic process.

- Adaptive Information Processing: EMDR is guided by the Adaptive Information Processing (AIP) model, which posits that the brain has a natural capacity to process and adaptively resolve disturbing memories when the processing system is unblocked.

EMDR has gained popularity for its ability to accelerate the processing of traumatic memories and alleviate symptoms such as flashbacks, nightmares, and hypervigilance.

4.3 Trauma-Focused Play Therapy for Children

Trauma doesn't discriminate by age, and children can be profoundly affected by traumatic experiences. Trauma-Focused Play Therapy is an evidence-based approach designed to help children process trauma through play and creative expression. Key elements of this approach include:

- Safe Environment: Creating a safe and nurturing environment is paramount in play therapy. Children need to feel secure before they can engage in therapeutic play.

- Therapeutic Toys and Materials: Play therapists use a variety of toys and materials to facilitate expression and communication, including art supplies, puppets, and sand trays.

- Symbolic Play: Children often use symbolic play to represent their experiences and emotions, allowing them to explore and make sense of trauma indirectly.

- Non-Directive Approach: Play therapists take a non-directive stance, allowing children to lead the play and express themselves at their own pace.

- Processing Trauma Narratives: Over time, children may use play to construct and share their trauma narratives, helping them gain a sense of mastery and understanding.

Trauma-Focused Play Therapy recognizes that children may not have the verbal skills to express their trauma directly. Instead, it offers a safe and developmentally appropriate way for them to work through their experiences and emotions.

In conclusion, evidence-based approaches are the backbone of effective trauma treatment. Whether using Cognitive-Behavioral Therapy to reframe thought patterns, Eye Movement Desensitization and Reprocessing to reprocess traumatic memories, or Trauma-Focused Play Therapy to help children heal, these tools in the trauma treatment toolbox provide therapists with a diverse set of strategies to support clients on their path to recovery. Each approach is tailored to address the unique needs and experiences of trauma survivors, offering hope and healing.

CHAPTER 5: MINDFULNESS AND GROUNDING TECHNIQUES

In the journey towards healing from trauma, the mind can often be a turbulent sea of distressing memories, emotions, and sensations. In this chapter, we delve into the therapeutic tools of mindfulness and grounding techniques – essential components of the Trauma Treatment Toolbox – that offer clients a lifeline to calm the storm within and reconnect with the present moment.

5.1 Grounding Exercises for Clients

Grounding techniques are a set of strategies that help individuals anchor themselves in the present moment, providing a sense of safety and stability. These exercises are particularly valuable for trauma survivors who may frequently experience distressing flashbacks or overwhelming emotions. Here are some effective grounding exercises for clients:

- 5-4-3-2-1 Exercise: This technique involves guiding clients to name five things they can see, four things they can touch, three things they can hear, two things they can smell, and one thing they can taste. It brings immediate awareness to the external environment.

- Breathing Exercises: Controlled breathing techniques, such as diaphragmatic breathing or the 4-7-8 technique, can help regulate the nervous system and reduce anxiety.

- Body Scan: Encouraging clients to mentally scan their body from head to toe, noting any areas of tension or discomfort, promotes self-awareness and relaxation.

- Grounding Objects: Clients can carry a small object (e.g., a stone, keychain, or smooth pebble) as a physical anchor to touch and focus on when feeling overwhelmed.

- Visualization: Guided imagery exercises, like imagining a safe place or a calming scene, can transport clients away from distressing thoughts and emotions.

Grounding techniques are versatile tools that can be adapted to suit individual client needs. They empower clients to regain control over their internal experiences and find stability in moments of distress.

5.2 Mindfulness Meditation in Trauma Healing

Mindfulness meditation is a practice rooted in ancient wisdom that has gained recognition in contemporary trauma therapy for its capacity to alleviate symptoms and foster resilience. At its core, mindfulness involves paying deliberate attention to the present moment without judgment. For trauma survivors, this practice can be transformative:

- Emotional Regulation: Mindfulness helps individuals recognize and manage their emotions more effectively. It creates a space between emotional triggers and reactions, allowing for more intentional responses.

- Reducing Avoidance: Trauma survivors often use avoidance as a coping mechanism. Mindfulness encourages facing distressing thoughts and sensations in a non-judgmental way, diminishing the need for avoidance.

- Increasing Self-Awareness: Mindfulness fosters self-awareness, helping clients notice early signs of distress and respond with self-compassion.

- Post-Traumatic Growth: While trauma is undoubtedly painful, some individuals experience post-traumatic growth – positive psychological changes that arise from trauma. Mindfulness can facilitate this growth by promoting a deeper sense of meaning and resilience.

Incorporating mindfulness meditation into trauma therapy requires patience and practice, but the benefits are profound. Clients can learn to observe their thoughts and emotions as passing events rather than defining characteristics, ultimately reducing suffering and enhancing well-being.

5.3 Yoga and Trauma Recovery

Yoga is a mind-body practice that combines physical postures, breath control, and meditation. In trauma recovery, yoga offers a holistic approach to healing by addressing both the physical and psychological aspects of trauma:

- Body Awareness: Trauma survivors often experience disconnection from their bodies. Yoga helps individuals reconnect with their physical sensations and promotes self-acceptance.

- Stress Reduction: The mindful movements and controlled breathing in yoga reduce the body's stress response, helping clients feel more relaxed and at ease.

- Empowerment: Yoga empowers clients by giving them a sense of agency over their bodies. It can help trauma survivors reclaim their physical autonomy.

- Self-Compassion: Practicing self-compassion is a fundamental aspect of yoga. It encourages clients to treat themselves with kindness and gentleness, counteracting self-blame and shame often associated with trauma.

Yoga practices can be adapted to suit all levels of physical ability, making it accessible to a wide range of clients. Trauma-informed yoga instructors are trained to create safe and nurturing environments, ensuring that the practice is supportive and empowering for trauma survivors.

In conclusion, mindfulness and grounding techniques are invaluable tools in the Trauma Treatment Toolbox. Grounding exercises offer immediate relief during moments of distress, mindfulness meditation fosters resilience and emotional regulation, and yoga provides a holistic approach to healing the mind and body. Integrating these practices into trauma therapy empowers clients to navigate their trauma with greater self-awareness, presence, and inner strength.

Chapter 6: Art and Expressive Therapies

Trauma often resides in the unspoken, the unsaid, and the unexpressed. In this chapter, we explore the transformative power of art and expressive therapies, including Art Therapy, Writing as a Therapeutic Tool, and Dance and Movement Therapy, as essential components of the Trauma Treatment Toolbox.

6.1 Using Art Therapy to Process Trauma

Art therapy is a unique form of psychotherapy that uses creative expression as a means of communication and healing. For trauma survivors, who may find verbal communication challenging or insufficient, art therapy offers a non-verbal outlet for processing and expressing their experiences. Here's how it works:

- Symbolic Expression: Trauma often defies direct description. Art therapy allows clients to use symbols, colors, and images to represent their feelings, memories, and sensations indirectly.

- Catharsis: The act of creating art can be cathartic, releasing pent-up emotions and providing relief from emotional distress.

- Empowerment: Art therapy gives clients a sense of control over their narrative. They can choose what to express and how to express it, promoting agency in the healing process.

- Externalization: Creating art helps clients externalize their internal experiences, making it easier to explore and process them.

- Metaphor and Insight: Art therapists can help clients explore the metaphors and symbols in their art, leading to insights and deeper self-understanding.

Art therapy is a versatile and adaptable approach that can be used with individuals of all ages, backgrounds, and artistic abilities. It taps into the creative potential within each person, fostering resilience and healing.

6.2 Writing as a Therapeutic Tool

The written word has a unique capacity to reveal, explore, and heal. Writing as a therapeutic tool, often referred to as journaling or narrative therapy, allows trauma survivors to externalize their experiences and emotions, create a coherent narrative, and find meaning in their trauma journey. Key aspects of this approach include:

- Journaling: Encouraging clients to keep a journal where they can write freely about their thoughts, emotions, and experiences provides a safe and private space for self-reflection.

- Letter Writing: Clients can write letters to their past or future selves, to the people who have hurt them, or to their trauma itself. This process can facilitate emotional release and closure.

- Narrative Reconstruction: Crafting a narrative of their trauma journey helps clients gain a sense of control over their story, transforming it from a jumbled mess into a coherent narrative.

- Therapeutic Writing Prompts: Therapists can provide specific prompts to guide clients in exploring their trauma from different angles, fostering insight and self-discovery.

- Poetry and Creative Writing: For some clients, creative writing or poetry can be a powerful means of self-expression and transformation.

Writing as a therapeutic tool allows clients to witness their own growth and resilience as they document their trauma journey. It provides a tangible record of progress and healing.

6.3 Dance and Movement Therapy for Trauma

Trauma can manifest not only in the mind but also in the body. Dance and movement therapy acknowledges this mind-body connection and uses movement as a tool for processing trauma. Here's how it works:

- Embodied Awareness: Clients learn to become more attuned to the sensations and movements of their bodies, helping them recognize and release physical tension and emotional blocks.

- Expressive Movement: Movement therapy encourages clients to express their emotions and experiences through dance and movement. It allows for the release of emotions that may be difficult to express verbally.

- Somatic Resourcing: Dance and movement therapy incorporates somatic resourcing techniques, which help clients build a sense of safety and stability in their bodies.

- Integration: Clients work to integrate their emotional and physical experiences, creating a more harmonious sense of self.

- Rhythmic Regulation: The use of rhythm and repetitive movement patterns can regulate the nervous system and reduce anxiety and hypervigilance.

Dance and movement therapy is particularly effective for clients who struggle with verbal expression or have a history of trauma that is stored in their bodies. It offers a non-threatening and holistic path to healing.

In conclusion, art and expressive therapies provide trauma survivors with diverse avenues for self-expression, healing, and transformation. Art therapy allows for non-verbal expression and symbolic representation, writing as a therapeutic tool fosters insight and narrative reconstruction, and dance and movement therapy bridges the mind-body connection, addressing trauma from a holistic perspective. These approaches in the Trauma Treatment Toolbox empower clients to embark on a creative and healing journey towards recovery and resilience.

Chapter 7: Family and Group Therapy

Trauma doesn't affect just individuals; it ripples through families and communities. This chapter explores the vital roles that family and group therapy play in the Trauma Treatment Toolbox, offering support, healing, and resilience to those affected by trauma.

7.1 Healing Family Dynamics After Trauma

When a family member experiences trauma, it can have profound effects on the entire family system. Family therapy provides a safe and collaborative space for family members to explore and address the impact of trauma on their relationships. Here are key aspects of healing family dynamics after trauma:

- Communication: Trauma can disrupt healthy communication within families. Family therapy helps family members learn effective communication skills, fostering understanding and empathy.

- Roles and Boundaries: Trauma can alter family roles and boundaries. Therapy helps identify and redefine these roles, creating healthier dynamics.

- Education: Family therapy can provide education about trauma, its effects, and strategies for supporting the trauma survivor.

- Emotional Processing: Family members can process their own feelings related to the trauma, including guilt, anger, and sadness, in a supportive and therapeutic environment.

- Conflict Resolution: Addressing conflicts that may arise within the family as a result of the trauma is a crucial component of family therapy.

- Rebuilding Trust: Trauma often erodes trust within families. Therapy can help rebuild trust by fostering open and honest communication.

Family therapy recognizes that healing is not an individual process but a collective one that involves the entire family unit. It empowers families to work together to support their loved ones on their journey to recovery.

7.2 Support Groups for Trauma Survivors

Support groups are invaluable for trauma survivors as they provide a sense of belonging, validation, and understanding. These groups offer a space where individuals can share their experiences, challenges, and triumphs with others who have gone through similar ordeals. Key elements of support groups for trauma survivors include:

- Validation: Group members often find comfort in knowing that they are not alone and that their experiences are understood and validated by others who have faced trauma.

- Empowerment: Support groups empower survivors to take control of their healing journey. Sharing their stories and hearing about others' progress fosters hope and resilience.

- Education: Support groups often include psychoeducation sessions, helping participants learn about the effects of trauma and providing them with coping strategies.

- Peer Support: The sense of camaraderie in support groups can be a powerful source of strength. Members support and encourage each other, reducing feelings of isolation.

- Safety: Support groups provide a safe and non-judgmental space where individuals can express their thoughts and feelings without fear of stigma.

Support groups can take various forms, including in-person meetings, online forums, or even phone-based groups. They offer trauma survivors a lifeline of understanding and connection.

7.3 Incorporating Trauma-Informed Care in Group Settings

Trauma-informed care extends beyond individual therapy and should be incorporated into group settings as well. Whether it's a support group, a school, or a community organization, following trauma-informed principles ensures that the environment is safe and respectful for all participants. Key elements of trauma-informed care in group settings include:

- Safety: Group leaders must prioritize physical and emotional safety for all participants. This may involve setting ground rules, ensuring privacy, and creating a welcoming atmosphere.

- Choice and Control: Trauma survivors should be given choices and control over their participation in group activities. They should never be forced into situations that trigger distress.

- Empowerment: Encouraging group members to actively participate in decisions related to the group fosters a sense of empowerment.

- Cultural Sensitivity: Group leaders should be culturally sensitive and aware of the diverse backgrounds and experiences of participants.

- Avoiding Re-Traumatization: Group activities and discussions should be designed to avoid re-traumatization and triggers. Leaders should be prepared to intervene if someone becomes distressed.

- Trauma-Informed Language: The use of trauma-informed language and communication is vital to avoid inadvertently causing harm.

Incorporating trauma-informed care into group settings ensures that all participants, whether they are trauma survivors or not, feel respected, supported, and safe.

Whether it's healing family dynamics, finding support in a group, or incorporating trauma-informed care in group settings, these approaches empower individuals and communities to heal, grow, and thrive in the aftermath of trauma.

CHAPTER 8: PHARMACOTHERAPY AND TRAUMA

In the multifaceted landscape of trauma treatment, pharmacotherapy plays a significant role in alleviating symptoms and supporting individuals on their path to recovery. This chapter explores the use of medications as a vital component of the Trauma Treatment Toolbox.

8.1 Medications for Trauma-Related Symptoms

Medications are often prescribed to address specific trauma-related symptoms, particularly when they significantly impact an individual's daily functioning or well-being. While medications don't directly "cure" trauma, they can help manage distressing symptoms, making it easier for individuals to engage in therapy and other healing modalities. Common symptoms that may be targeted with medications include:

- Anxiety: Selective serotonin reuptake inhibitors (SSRIs) and benzodiazepines are frequently prescribed to alleviate anxiety symptoms.

- Depression: Antidepressants, such as SSRIs or serotonin-norepinephrine reuptake inhibitors (SNRIs), can help manage depressive symptoms often associated with trauma.

- Nightmares and Sleep Disturbances: Medications like prazosin may be prescribed to reduce nightmares and improve sleep quality.

- Hyperarousal and Flashbacks: Antipsychotic medications or certain mood stabilizers can help manage symptoms of hyperarousal and flashbacks.

It's important to note that medication should always be prescribed and monitored by a qualified healthcare provider with expertise in trauma treatment. The choice of medication depends on the specific symptoms and needs of the individual, and treatment is often tailored to the person's unique experiences and response to medication.

8.2 The Role of Psychopharmacology in Trauma Treatment

Psychopharmacology, the study of how medications affect mood, behavior, and mental processes, plays a crucial role in trauma treatment. Trauma can lead to alterations in brain chemistry and function, and psychopharmacology seeks to address these neurobiological changes. Here are some key considerations regarding the role of psychopharmacology in trauma treatment:

- Neurotransmitter Regulation: Trauma can disrupt the balance of neurotransmitters in the brain. Medications can help regulate these neurotransmitters to alleviate symptoms like anxiety and depression.

- Stabilizing Mood: Trauma survivors may experience intense mood swings. Medications can help stabilize mood and reduce emotional dysregulation.

- Enhancing Cognitive Function: Some medications can improve cognitive function, which is often impaired in individuals with a history of trauma.

- Comorbidity: Trauma often co-occurs with other mental health conditions like depression, anxiety, and substance use disorders. Medication can address these comorbidities, making therapy more effective.

- Safety and Functionality: For individuals who are in crisis or struggling to function due to severe symptoms, medication can provide a bridge to stability and safety.

It's important to emphasize that medication is not a standalone treatment for trauma but is typically used in conjunction with psychotherapy and other therapeutic approaches.

8.3 Integrating Medication with Psychotherapy

The integration of medication with psychotherapy is a powerful approach in trauma treatment. Psychotherapy helps individuals process their traumatic experiences, develop coping strategies, and gain insight into their emotions and behaviors. Medication can support this process by reducing symptoms that may otherwise hinder engagement in therapy. Key points in integrating medication with psychotherapy include:

- Collaboration: Effective communication between the prescribing healthcare provider and the therapist is essential. They work together to create a comprehensive treatment plan.

- Monitoring: Regular monitoring of medication effectiveness and potential side effects is crucial. Adjustments to medication may be made as needed.

- Psychoeducation: Clients are educated about their medications, including how they work and potential side effects, to promote informed decision-making.

- Personalized Treatment: Medication choices are personalized based on the individual's symptoms, needs, and treatment goals.

- Holistic Approach: The combination of medication and therapy offers a holistic approach that addresses both the physiological and psychological aspects of trauma.

It's important to approach medication as a tool within the broader context of trauma treatment. It is not a "quick fix" but rather a supportive element that can help individuals engage more effectively in the therapeutic process.

In conclusion, pharmacotherapy is a valuable component of the Trauma Treatment Toolbox, providing relief from distressing symptoms and supporting individuals in their journey toward healing. When used in conjunction with psychotherapy and other therapeutic modalities, medications can contribute significantly to the recovery process for trauma survivors.

Chapter 9: Resilience and Post-Traumatic Growth

Trauma, while profoundly challenging, can also be a catalyst for resilience and personal growth. This chapter explores the concepts of resilience, post-traumatic growth, and the spiritual and existential aspects of trauma within the Trauma Treatment Toolbox.

9.1 Fostering Resilience in Trauma Survivors

Resilience is the ability to adapt and bounce back from adversity. Trauma survivors often demonstrate remarkable resilience in the face of overwhelming experiences. Therapists can play a pivotal role in fostering resilience in their clients:

- Building Coping Skills: Helping clients develop healthy coping mechanisms, such as emotion regulation and stress management, is a cornerstone of resilience.

- Narrative Reconstruction: Encouraging clients to reframe their traumatic experiences and find meaning within them can lead to a greater sense of resilience.

- Social Support: Fostering a support network of friends and family can provide a crucial buffer against the effects of trauma.

- Self-Care: Emphasizing self-care practices, including exercise, mindfulness, and healthy nutrition, can promote physical and emotional well-being.

- Positive Psychology: Incorporating positive psychology interventions, such as gratitude exercises and strengths-based approaches, can enhance resilience.

- Goal Setting: Collaborating with clients to set and work towards achievable goals can instill a sense of purpose and motivation.

Resilience is not a fixed trait; it can be cultivated and strengthened through therapeutic interventions and personal growth.

9.2 Understanding Post-Traumatic Growth

While trauma is undoubtedly painful, some individuals experience post-traumatic growth (PTG) – positive psychological changes that arise as a result of the struggle with trauma. PTG is not about denying the pain but finding opportunities for personal transformation and increased well-being. Key aspects of understanding PTG include:

- Five Domains of Growth: PTG often occurs in five domains: personal strength, new possibilities, relating to others, appreciation of life, and spiritual or existential growth.

- Change in Perspective: Trauma can lead individuals to reevaluate their values, priorities, and life goals, often resulting in a deeper appreciation of life.

- Increased Resilience: Individuals who experience PTG often report greater emotional resilience and an enhanced ability to navigate future challenges.

- Spiritual Growth: Some people find that trauma prompts them to explore or deepen their spiritual or existential beliefs, leading to a more profound sense of meaning and purpose.

- Self-Discovery: PTG can involve a process of self-discovery, where individuals learn more about their strengths, values, and capacities for growth.

Therapists can help clients recognize and harness the potential for growth within the trauma experience. This involves exploring the ways in which trauma has impacted their lives and identifying areas of positive change and personal development.

9.3 Navigating Spiritual and Existential Aspects of Trauma

Trauma often raises profound spiritual and existential questions. Clients may grapple with questions about the meaning of life, the nature of suffering, and their place in the universe. Addressing these aspects of trauma requires a sensitive and empathetic approach:

- Exploring Existential Questions: Encouraging clients to explore their existential concerns can lead to deeper self-understanding and meaning-making.

- Spiritual Support: For individuals with strong spiritual or religious beliefs, therapists can help them draw on their faith as a source of support and meaning.

- Mind-Body Connection: Recognizing the mind-body connection, where emotional pain is often experienced physically, can help clients integrate spiritual and existential aspects of trauma.

- Transcendence and Transformation: Trauma can prompt individuals to seek higher states of consciousness and transformation. Therapists can support this journey while ensuring it remains grounded and balanced.

- Respecting Diverse Beliefs: It's crucial for therapists to respect and acknowledge diverse spiritual and existential beliefs, ensuring that clients feel safe discussing these sensitive topics.

The spiritual and existential dimensions of trauma can be deeply transformative and offer opportunities for clients to find meaning, purpose, and transcendence in the face of adversity.

In conclusion, resilience and post-traumatic growth are powerful aspects of the Trauma Treatment Toolbox. Fostering resilience helps individuals navigate trauma with strength and adaptability, while understanding and facilitating post-traumatic growth allows clients to find meaning and transformation in the aftermath of trauma. Addressing the spiritual and existential dimensions of trauma acknowledges the profound questions and experiences that arise and supports clients in their search for deeper understanding and healing.

Chapter 10: Trauma-Informed Self-Care

In the world of trauma treatment, it's essential to remember that those who provide care and support to survivors are not immune to the impact of trauma. This chapter explores the critical importance of trauma-informed self-care for therapists and professionals in the field, addressing their well-being and resilience within the Trauma Treatment Toolbox.

10.1 Self-Care Strategies for Trauma Therapists

Trauma therapists often bear witness to painful and distressing stories. Without proper self-care, they risk experiencing secondary trauma or burnout. Here are some effective self-care strategies for trauma therapists:

- Supervision and Consultation: Regular supervision and consultation with experienced colleagues or supervisors provide a space to process difficult cases and emotions.

- Boundaries: Setting and maintaining clear professional boundaries is crucial to prevent emotional exhaustion. This includes managing caseloads and taking breaks between sessions.

- Self-Compassion: Practicing self-compassion allows therapists to be kind to themselves when they face challenges or make mistakes in their work.

- Mindfulness and Relaxation: Incorporating mindfulness and relaxation techniques into daily routines helps therapists manage stress and stay present in their work.

- Physical Health: Proper nutrition, exercise, and adequate sleep contribute to physical and emotional resilience.

- Hobbies and Interests: Engaging in hobbies and interests outside of work provides balance and enjoyment in life.

- Peer Support: Connecting with fellow therapists for mutual support and debriefing can be therapeutic.

Trauma therapists should view self-care as an ethical responsibility to ensure they can continue providing quality care to their clients.

10.2 Preventing Burnout in Trauma Work

Burnout is a real risk in trauma work due to the emotional and psychological demands of the profession. Preventing burnout requires proactive measures:

- Self-Assessment: Regularly assess your emotional and physical well-being. Recognize signs of burnout, such as emotional exhaustion, depersonalization, and reduced sense of personal accomplishment.

- Limit Exposure: While it's essential to empathize with clients, therapists should limit exposure to traumatic material outside of work hours.

- Supervision: Seek supervision and support to address any signs of burnout or secondary trauma promptly.

- Variety in Caseload: Consider balancing your caseload with a mix of trauma and non-trauma cases to reduce the emotional intensity of your work.

- Self-Reflection: Engage in self-reflection to explore your reactions to trauma work and gain insight into your emotional responses.

- Regular Breaks: Take regular breaks to recharge and rejuvenate. Vacations and time off are vital for preventing burnout.

Preventing burnout is essential not only for the well-being of therapists but also to ensure that they can continue to provide effective and compassionate care to their clients.

10.3 Building a Trauma-Informed Practice

Creating a trauma-informed practice involves integrating trauma awareness and sensitivity into every aspect of therapeutic work. Here's how therapists can build a trauma-informed practice:

- Education: Continually educate yourself about trauma, its effects, and evidence-based treatments.

- Screening and Assessment: Implement trauma-informed screening and assessment tools to identify trauma history and symptoms.

- Safe and Supportive Environment: Create a safe and supportive therapeutic environment that respects clients' autonomy and choices.

- Collaborative Treatment: Involve clients in the treatment planning process and respect their preferences and goals.

- Avoid Re-Traumatization: Be mindful of potential triggers or re-traumatization during therapy sessions.

- Trauma-Informed Language: Use trauma-informed language that is respectful and non-judgmental.

- Cultural Sensitivity: Recognize the impact of culture on trauma experiences and treatment approaches.

A trauma-informed practice not only benefits clients but also contributes to the well-being and resilience of therapists by promoting ethical, compassionate, and effective care.

In conclusion, trauma-informed self-care is a vital component of the Trauma Treatment Toolbox, recognizing that those who provide care to trauma survivors need support and resilience to continue their valuable work. By practicing self-care, preventing burnout, and building a trauma-informed practice, therapists and professionals can ensure that they are well-equipped to support and empower their clients on their journey towards healing and recovery.

CONCLUSION: UNPACKING THE TRAUMA TREATMENT TOOLBOX

As we conclude this journey through the Trauma Treatment Toolbox, we reflect on the profound importance of understanding, compassion, and resilience in the face of trauma. This book has explored a diverse array of tools and approaches for addressing trauma, recognizing that healing is a complex and deeply personal journey.

Throughout these chapters, we have delved into the core principles of trauma-informed care, from understanding the neurological and psychological impacts of trauma to the art of fostering resilience and promoting post-traumatic growth. We've explored the role of self-care for therapists, recognizing that those who provide support to trauma survivors must also nurture their own well-being.

The Trauma Treatment Toolbox has offered a comprehensive guide for therapists, healthcare providers, and individuals seeking to better understand and address trauma. It emphasizes the importance of a holistic and individualized approach to treatment, recognizing that no two trauma journeys are the same.

As we look back on this journey, several key themes emerge:

1. Empathy and Compassion: Throughout the pages of this book, the importance of empathy and compassion in trauma treatment is a constant thread. It is through these qualities that healing begins.

2. Resilience and Growth: Trauma is not merely a story of pain and suffering but also one of resilience and potential for growth. Trauma survivors can emerge from their experiences stronger and more resilient than before.

3. Self-Care: We have learned that self-care is not a luxury but a necessity, especially for those engaged in trauma work. It is a critical tool for preventing burnout and maintaining the capacity to provide effective care.

4. Diversity and Cultural Sensitivity: Trauma affects individuals from all walks of life and cultural backgrounds. A trauma-informed approach must be sensitive to these diverse experiences and beliefs.

5. Collaboration and Support: Healing from trauma is often a collaborative process. The support of therapists, friends, families, and support groups is invaluable in the journey toward recovery.

In closing, the Trauma Treatment Toolbox is not a static set of tools but a dynamic and evolving resource. The field of trauma therapy continually adapts and grows, drawing on new research, insights, and practices. We encourage you to continue your exploration of trauma treatment, to seek ongoing education, and to approach this work with a heart full of empathy and a commitment to making the world a safer and more healing place for all who have experienced trauma.

Remember that healing is possible. Trauma does not define a person's entire story, but it is a chapter in a larger narrative of resilience, strength, and hope. By applying the knowledge and tools shared in this book, we can contribute to the healing journey of trauma survivors and help them write a new chapter filled with possibility and growth.

Milton Keynes UK
Ingram Content Group UK Ltd.
UKHW020942221123
433051UK00020B/990